Songs for Many Seasons

Nine Anthems for the Church Year

Colin Mawby

Kevin Mayhew

We hope you enjoy the music in *Songs for Many Seasons*. Further copies are available from your local music or christian bookshop.

In case of difficulty, please contact the publisher direct by writing to:

The Sales Department
KEVIN MAYHEW LTD
Rattlesden
Bury St Edmunds
Suffolk IP30 0SZ

Phone   0449 737978
Fax   0449 737834

Access and Visa facilities are available for payment.
Please ask for our complete catalogue of outstanding Church Music.

First published in Great Britain by

KEVIN MAYHEW LTD
Rattlesden
Bury St Edmunds
Suffolk IP30 0SZ

ISBN 0 86209 191 8

Cover illustration by Michael Carlo
Cover design by Graham Johnstone
Printed and bound in Great Britain by
J. B. Offset Printers (Marks Tey) Limited

CONTENTS

The Royal Road Has Been Prepared   1

When Mary Brought Her Child   2

Faithful Magi Came From Foreign Lands   3

Lord, Twelve Were Called   4

The Lord Who Rode In Triumph   5

The Stranger On The Shore   6

The Lord Ascends Above   7

O Holy Paradox Of Love   8

Jesus Christ, The Apple Tree   9

FOREWORD

These Seasonal Songs, which are set to new texts by Jeremy Davies, Precentor of Salisbury Cathedral, incorporate some of the finest Plainsong hymns and are designed to suit a variety of liturgical situations.

Although I have included accompaniments for the plainsong, those choirs which prefer their chant unaccompanied may leave them out.

In the fourth song, *Lord, twelve were called,* choirs may use either setting or both, in which case verse two should be sung in the simpler version and verse four in the more elaborate.

COLIN MAWBY

1

Advent
The Royal Road Has Been Prepared

Text JEREMY DAVIES   Music COLIN MAWBY

raise the dead, give blind ones

Man.

sight, give blind ones sight, makes his com-ing ho-ly

day de-pend on Ma-ry's yea or nay.

Ped.

Sopranos and Altos

3. And when the Lord who made all things comes to his own, new gifts to bring,

he's found up - on a mai-den's breast, a babe, through whom God's world is blest.

With movement

mf

4. And when this babe, through suff - 'ring

mf

With movement

mf

Ped.

grown, comes once a-gain to claim, to claim his own, 'twill be his

love that sows the seeds of mer-cy, of mer-cy, where he

in - ter - cedes, where he in - ter - cedes.

2

Feast of the Purification (Candlemas)
When Mary Brought Her Child

Text JEREMY DAVIES   Music COLIN MAWBY

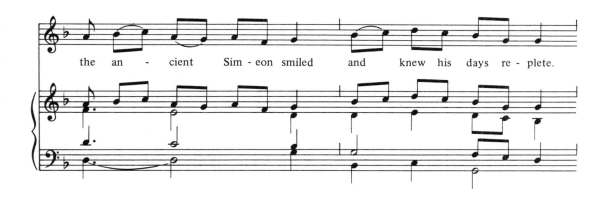

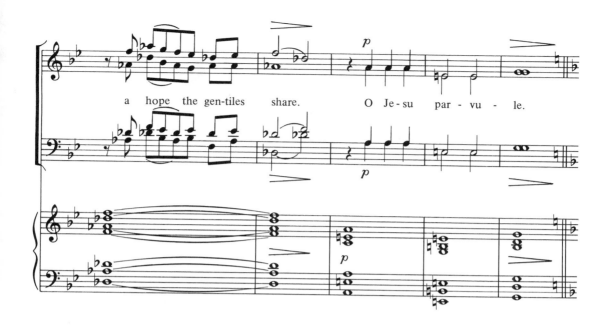

a hope the gen-tiles share. O Je-su par-vu-le.

Tenors and Basses

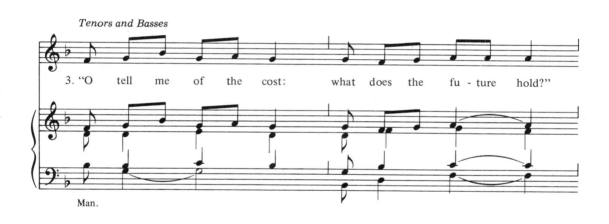

3. "O tell me of the cost: what does the fu-ture hold?"

Man.

"More cost-ly than a dove, your pre-cious child is sold.

These ti-ny arms out-stretched our na-ture to en-fold." O Je-su par-vu-le.

Very grand *f*

4. "And when they lance his side And try to snuff this

flame, your soul will share the smart

All reeds

Ped.

12

3

Epiphany
Faithful Magi Came From Foreign Lands

Text JEREMY DAVIES   Music COLIN MAWBY

* Sopranos may sing F♯ instead of A.

hom - age, their hom - age to him   paid;

They   left   with joy, their   souls   re -

lieved,

For with their gifts their woes they'd laid,

for with their gifts their woes they'd laid.

Tenors and Basses

3. And when this child, to man-hood grown,

re - ceived from John the cleans - ing rite,

the cleans - ing was not his a - lone,

for his o - be - dience gave us sight.

Allegro

4. True sight, to

see, true sight to see what God has done

in chang-ing wa - ter, wa-ter in - to

wine, in

19

heal - ing bo-dies racked with pain,

più f

più f

in warm-ing hearts; yes, e - ven mine,

più f

slower
ff

molto rit.

In warm-ing hearts; yes, e - ven mine.

ff

slower

molto rit.

ff

4

Lent

Lord, Twelve Were Called

Text JEREMY DAVIES   Music COLIN MAWBY

An alternative (SATB) setting for verses 2 and 4 will be found on page 29.

Andante

S. 2. Lord, can it be that we are called to fol - low

A. 2. Lord, can it be that we are called to fol - low

T. 2. Lord, can it be that we are called to fol - low

B. 2. Lord, can it be that we are called to fol - low

Andante

in this ho - ly way, to take a cross, des -

in this ho - ly way, to take a cross, des -

in this ho - ly way, to take a cross, des -

in this ho - ly way, cross, des -

pite   our   fault, and tell   your   sto - ry   here   to - day?

Tenors and Basses

3. Lord, you once gave your spi - rit's grace

Man.

to those who joined the Christ - ian band;

O, give us in our time and place

the gifts we need to make our stand:

love with - in us move; give hu - mour, cour - age,

love with - in us move; give hu - mour, cour - age,

love with - in us move; give hu - mour, cour - age,

love with - in us move; cour - age,

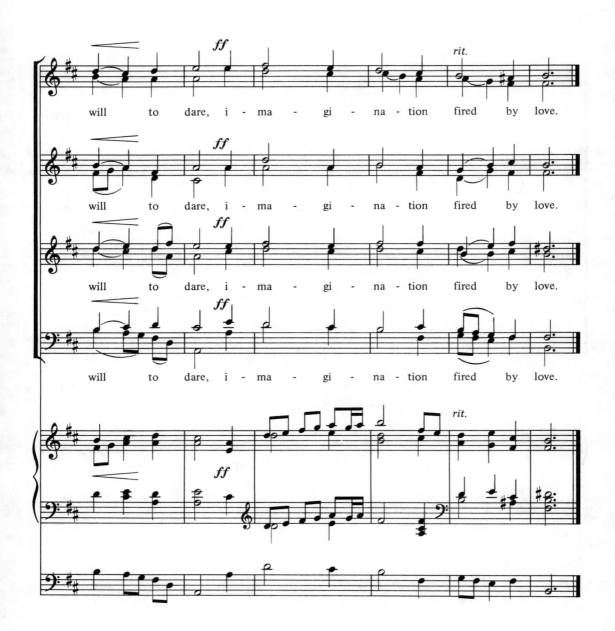

will   to   dare,   i - ma - gi - na - tion   fired   by   love.

will   to   dare,   i - ma - gi - na - tion   fired   by   love.

will   to   dare,   i - ma - gi - na - tion   fired   by   love.

will   to   dare,   i - ma - gi - na - tion   fired   by   love.

Alternative version (verses 2 and 4)

2. Lord, can it be that we are called to fol - low in this ho - ly way, to take a - cross, des - pite our fault, and tell your sto - ry here to - day?

4. Your word, your sac - ra - ments and prayer, faith, hope and love with - in us move; give hu - mour, cour - age, will to dare, i - ma - gi - na - tion fired by love.

5
Passiontide
The Lord Who Rode In Triumph

Text JEREMY DAVIES Music COLIN MAWBY

Je - sus Christ is raised, men may stop and won - der, men may stop and won - der: so will God be praised, God be praised.

Sopranos and Altos

3. The sol‑diers, lit‑tle heed‑ing what's a‑bove their head,

Man.

they gam‑ble for a seam‑less robe when their man is dead.

"Life's but a game of chance," "Pup‑pets on a string,"

un‑less the one who's bleed‑ing is in‑deed the King.

5. Poor Pilate paused to wonder why the world was made; Man.

soldiers, looking crosswards, knew the price was paid.

"'Tis finished," Jesus said. God's creation now

has by his death been freed from sin: Jesus shows us how.

Those far off and near   God's love re - con -

ciles   us,   God's love re - con - ciles   us

cast - ing out all   fear,   all   fear.

6

Easter

The Stranger On The Shore

Text JEREMY DAVIES   Music COLIN MAWBY

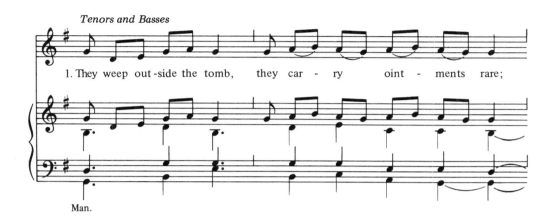

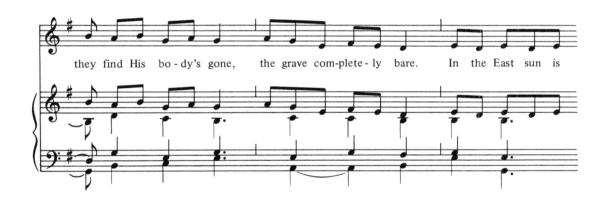

43

love for - gives your pride."

"Je - sus, I be -

Man.

lieve in you,　　my　Lord, my　God,　　make

my　heart　true."

Ped.

44

7
Ascension
The Lord Ascends Above

Text JEREMY DAVIES   Music COLIN MAWBY

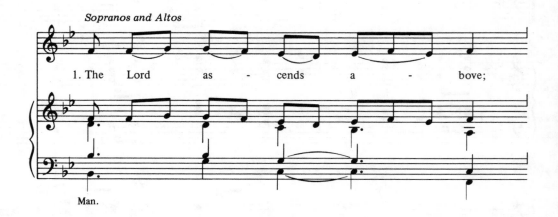

2. He came that men might see God's grace in hu-man-ness. He now as-cends, that we might share, might share his god-li-ness.

3. The work which was be-gun when first cre-a-tion stirred

Stately

Ped.

Man.

49

is fin - ished by the Son, God's first and fi - nal Word.

4. That Word em-powers the

Man.

Church to be Christ's pre-sence here,

sign for our God - ward search,

sign that his love is near,

is near, his love is near, near.

Ped.

8

Pentecost

O Holy Paradox Of Love

Text JEREMY DAVIES   Music COLIN MAWBY

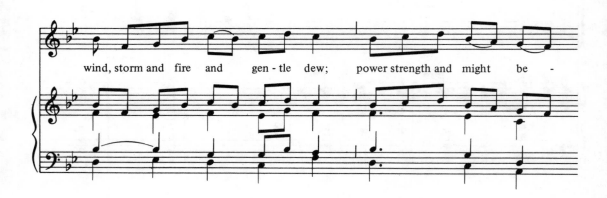

2. Then turn to prayer our deep - est groan, in words too deep too deep for sighs: through you our long - ings are made known and

"Ab - ba, Fa - ther," is our prize.

Tenors and Basses

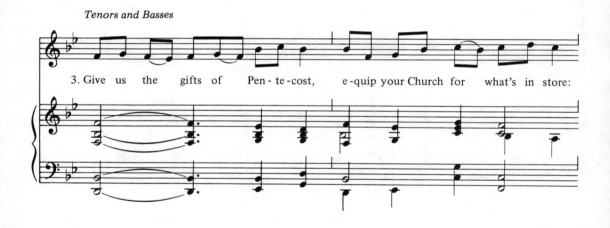

3. Give us the gifts of Pen - te -cost, e -quip your Church for what's in store:

with - out your guid - ance we are lost, but with your grace we need no more.

4. Of all the gifts on us en-dowed, en-dowed (quite un-de - served but much in need) set love as a je-wel in the

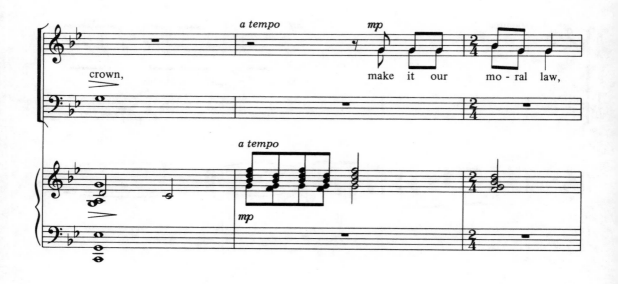

crown,

make it our mo - ral law,

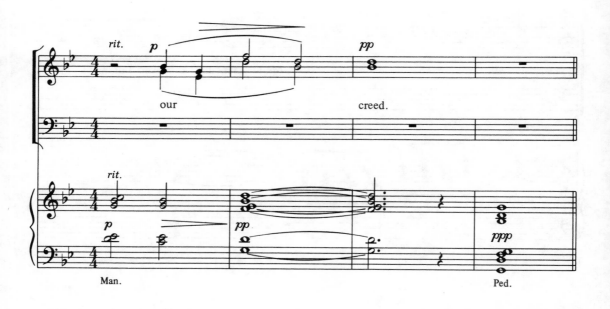

our creed.

Man.

Ped.

5. Your Church has marred your con - stant love

Man.

by our mis-us-ings of your grace; give u-ni-ty, O

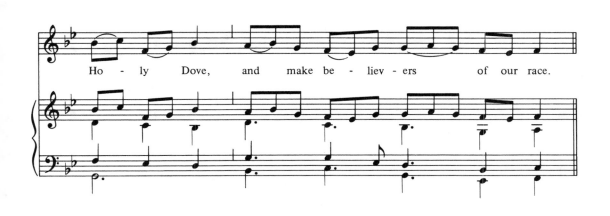

Ho - ly Dove, and make be - liev - ers of our race.

6. O ho - ly pa - ra - dox of love, wind,

storm and fire and gen - tle dew; power

strength and might be - low a - bove, un -

seen but known, Cre - a - tor new.

9

General

Jesus Christ, The Apple Tree

Text Unknown, from the *Collection of Joshua Smith*, New Hampshire (1784)
Music COLIN MAWBY

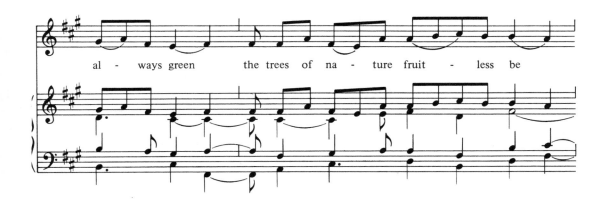

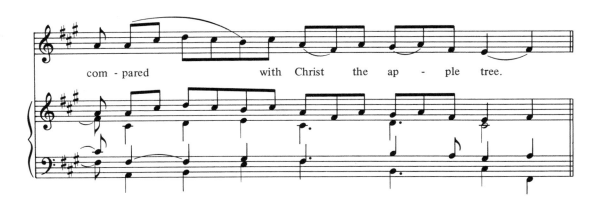

Either line may divide, depending upon available singers.

Sopranos and Altos

3. For hap - pi - ness I long have sought;

Man.

and plea - sure dear - ly I have bought:

I missed of all; but now I see

'tis found in Christ the ap - ple tree.

61

ap - ple tree, of Je-sus Christ the ap - ple tree.

5. This fruit doth make my soul to thrive, it keeps my

dy - ing faith a - live; which makes my soul in haste to be

Either line may divide, depending upon available resourses.